How your child's LeapReader™ works

Helps children build **reading**, **writing**, and **listening skills** with an interactive book reader and audio player. LeapReader is designed to enhance vocabulary development and reading comprehension to help children become confident, independent readers and writers.

LeapReader modes

Audio Books	Music	Trivia Fun

Home

Headphone jack

Volume up/down

Play/Pause

Forward/Back

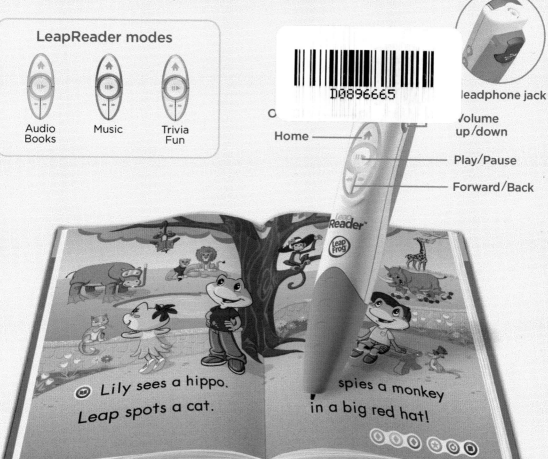

@ Lily sees a hippo.
Leap spots a cat.

spies a monkey
in a big red hat!

 Read the Page

 Sound It / Say It

 Repeat

 Game

 Say It / Sound It / Spell It

 Stop

LeapReader™
Reading and Writing System*

Get Ready to Read

Develop reading basics and other essential preschool skills with durable board books and more.

- Letters & sounds
- Number basics
- Early vocabulary
- Preschool skills

Early Reading

Build core reading skills with word building and phonics, including "sound it out" word-by-word support.

- Core phonics skills
- Vowel sounds
- Sight words
- Basic sentences

Read & Write

Write letters, numbers, words and equations. Solve mathematics problems and puzzles.

- Uppercase & lowercase letters
- Stroke order
- Mathematics
- Problem solving

The LeapReader™ Reading and Writing System guides children through their learn-to-read journey!

Read on Your Own

Grow reading skills with engaging stories focused on vocabulary and reading comprehension.

- Reading comprehension
- Advanced vocabulary
- Longer story text
- Complex sentences

Learn through Reading

Explore subjects like science, geography and creativity with puzzles, maps and more.

- Science
- Geography
- Creativity
- Puzzles

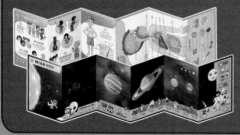   

Audio books, learning songs & trivia fun!

Download 100+ stories, songs and more to help build listening skills.

- Listening comprehension
- Vocabulary development
- Story structure
- Music appreciation
- Imagining stories

Lily sees a hippo.

Leap spots a cat.

Tad spies a monkey
in a big red hat!

His first big race was the Dinoco 400. He raced with Chick Hicks and The King. They finished at the same time.

"No way!" Lightning thought.

... and Cinderella had everything she needed to go to the ball! She had a pretty dress and glass slippers, too.

"You'll have only until midnight," the Fairy Godmother told Cinderella.

📖 Dory and Marlin swim into a
jellyfish forest. Jellyfish can sting.

"Do not touch the tentacles," Marlin tells Dory.

 "I can be a fisherman. I can get fish in a net."

"And I can rest on the deck when I get wet," said Leap.

Rhyme Time

Word Fuser

c→at

DJ Word

Tune Time

c

r

Build over 100 simple words with 40 cards!

400+ interactive responses and 5 learning games. Includes storage box for on-the-go fun!

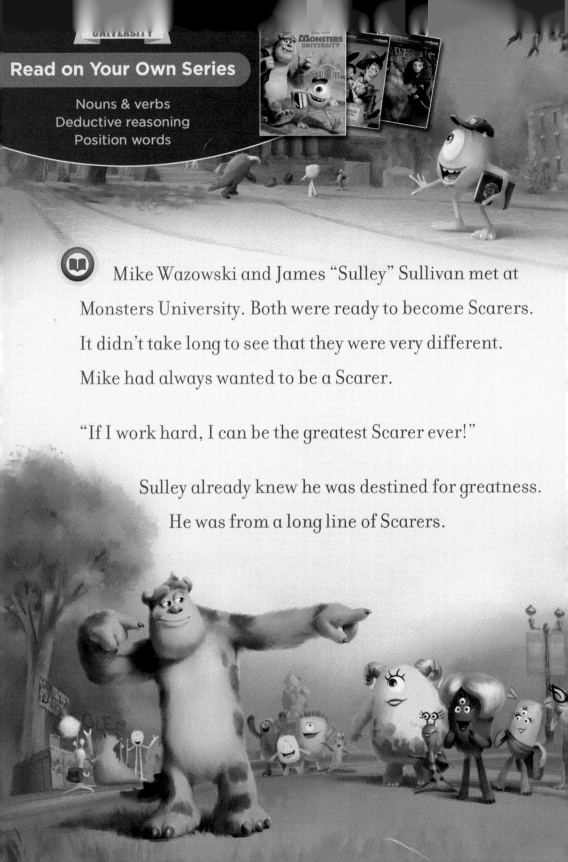

Mike Wazowski and James "Sulley" Sullivan met at
Monsters University. Both were ready to become Scarers.
It didn't take long to see that they were very different.
Mike had always wanted to be a Scarer.

"If I work hard, I can be the greatest Scarer ever!"

Sulley already knew he was destined for greatness.
He was from a long line of Scarers.

"Study all you want, little guy. A monster like you
will never be a Scarer." Sulley laughed.

It was too late, though. The lords of the three clans had brought their sons to compete for my hand—numpties, the lot of them. But I wasn't ready, and Mum, she wouldn't listen. So I decided to enter the competition to shoot for my own hand.

I won, too! But Mum was furious.

They raced up the stairs.

"Stop!" cried the mummy.

"Stop!" cried the witch.

"Stop!" cried the vampire.

"Let's find Velma, Fred, and
Daphne. Then we'll get out of here,"
said Shaggy.

SCOOBY-DOO!

Read on Your Own Series

Question words • Plot elements
Feelings & emotions

With a loud clunk, the time machine came to a stop. Quigley, Leap, and Zoey looked out into a strange world.

CHOMP!

HERBIVORES

OMNIVORES

CARNIVORES

LEAP AND THE LOST
DINOSAUR

Read & Learn!
World Map
JUMBO PUZZLE

Read to Learn!
SOLAR
SYSTEM

LEAP AND THE LOST
DINOSAUR

Learn through Reading Series

Dinosaur facts • Science skills
Fossils

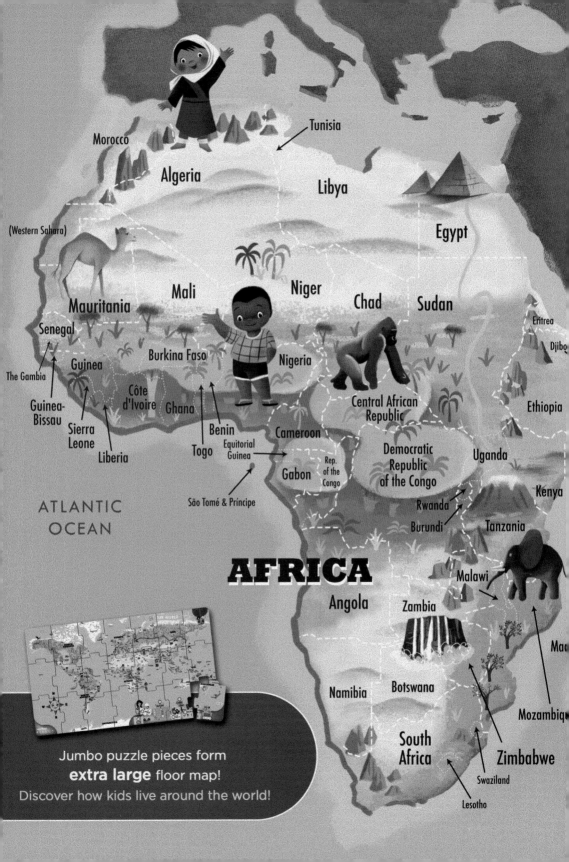

Morocco

Tunisia

Algeria

Libya

Egypt

(Western Sahara)

Mali

Niger

Chad

Sudan

Eritrea

Djibo

Mauritania

Senegal

Burkina Faso

Nigeria

Ethiopia

The Gambia

Guinea

Côte d'Ivoire

Ghana

Central African Republic

Uganda

Guinea-Bissau

Benin

Cameroon

Kenya

Sierra Leone

Togo

Equitorial Guinea

Democratic Republic of the Congo

Liberia

Gabon

Rep. of the Congo

Rwanda

São Tomé & Príncipe

Burundi

Tanzania

ATLANTIC OCEAN

AFRICA

Malawi

Angola

Zambia

Namibia

Botswana

Maa

Mozambiq

Jumbo puzzle pieces form **extra large** floor map!

Discover how kids live around the world!

South Africa

Zimbabwe

Swaziland

Lesotho

Interactive World Map Puzzle

Learn through Reading Series

World geography • Map skills
World languages

Where AM I?

INDIAN
OCEAN

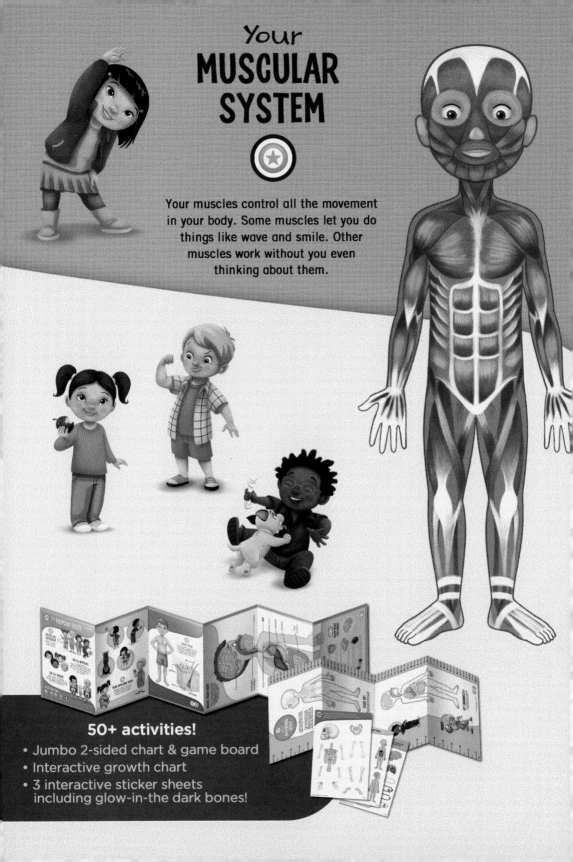

Your
MUSCULAR
SYSTEM

Your muscles control all the movement in your body. Some muscles let you do things like wave and smile. Other muscles work without you even thinking about them.

50+ activities!

- Jumbo 2-sided chart & game board
- Interactive growth chart
- 3 interactive sticker sheets including glow-in-the dark bones!

Interactive
HUMAN BODY
Discovery Pack

Learn through Reading Series

Human body facts • Body systems
Nutrition & diet

your SKELETAL SYSTEM

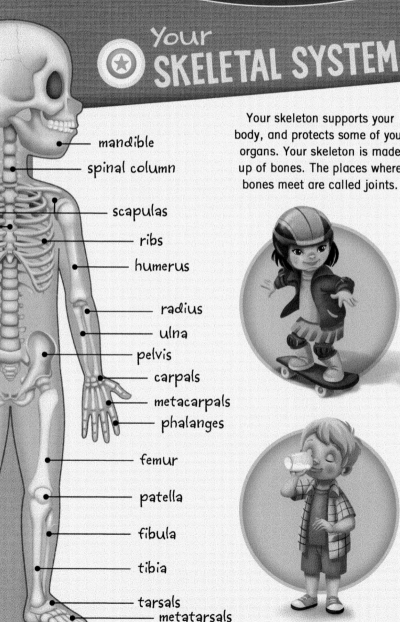

- cranium
- mandible
- spinal column
- clavicle
- scapulas
- sternum
- ribs
- humerus
- radius
- ulna
- pelvis
- carpals
- metacarpals
- phalanges
- femur
- patella
- fibula
- tibia
- tarsals
- metatarsals
- phalanges

Your skeleton supports your body, and protects some of your organs. Your skeleton is made up of bones. The places where bones meet are called joints.

NEW for **LeapReader**™

Read & Write

Write letters, numbers, words and equations.
Solve mathematics problems and puzzles.
Get stroke-by-stroke guidance to form letters correctly.

Check out your included LeapFrog™ Learning Paper!

- Uppercase & lowercase letters
- Stroke order
- Mathematics
- Problem solving

"Why would sheep be practicing skateboarding?" asked Dot.

"To get better at it!" said Curly Q. "They'll be done soon."

♫ Listening ♫♪

Audio books can help develop listening, comprehension and vocabulary skills and spark the imagination!

Sing along with fun learning songs anytime, anywhere!

Connect your LeapReader to your computer and go to leapfrog.com/connect to download audio books, songs, and more!

Connect to download your audio book bundle, music album and trivia fun!

- Listening comprehension
- Vocabulary development
- Story structure
- Music appreciation
- Imagining stories